Forward Learning

Math Readiness

K

Table of Contents

- Counting to 20
- Canadian money, time
- 2D and 3D shapes
- Patterning, classification
- And much more!

Margaret Ann Hawkins, B.Ed.

Let's Celebrate Numbers!

1

How many cakes do you see?

Colour the picture.

Trace the number.

Print the number.

Let's Celebrate Numbers!

2

How many balloons do you see? 2

Trace the number.

2 2 2 2 2 2 2 2 2 2 2

Print the number.

Print the number.

Let's Celebrate Numbers!

3

How many pizzas do you see?

Colour the picture.

Trace the number.

3 3 3 3 3 3 3 3 3

3 3 3 3 3 3 3 3 3

Print the number.

Let's Celebrate Numbers!

4

How many presents do you see? 4

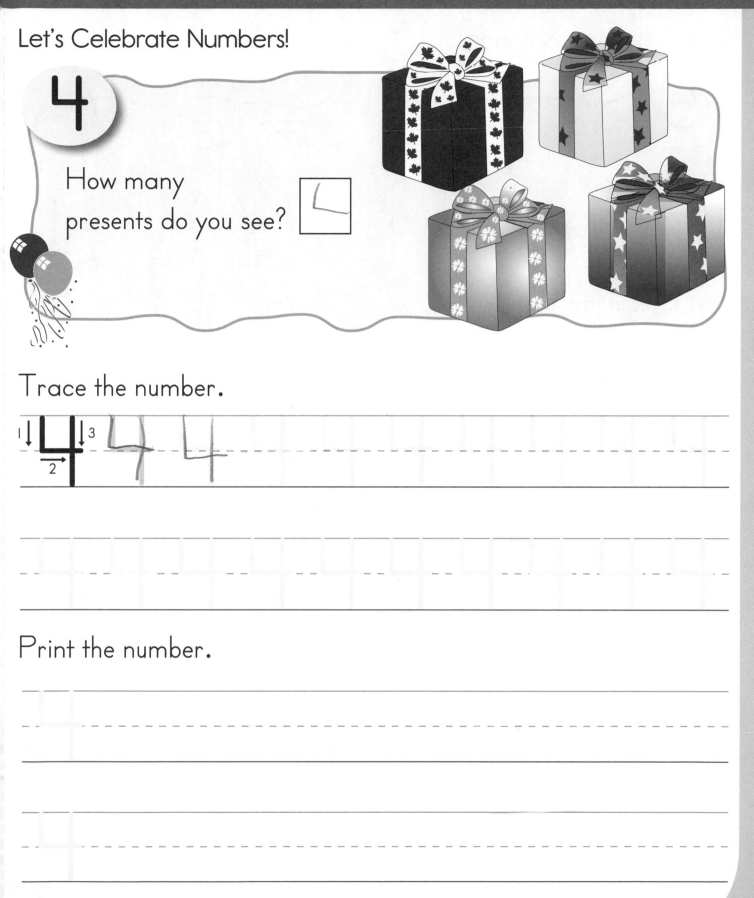

Trace the number.

↓1 ↓3 **4** 4 4
→2

Print the number.

Let's Celebrate Numbers!

5

How many drinks do you see? ☐

Colour the picture.

Trace the number.

5 5 5 5 5 5 5 5 5 5

5 5 5 5 5 5 5 5 5 5

Print the number.

5

5

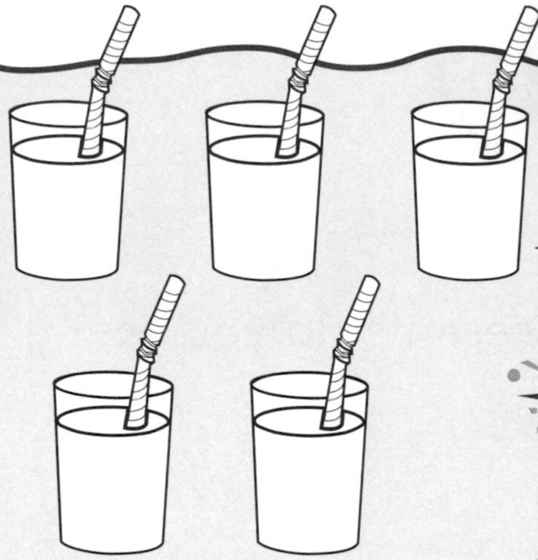

Let's Celebrate Numbers!

6

How many ice cream cones do you see?

Trace the number.

6 6

Print the number.

Let's Celebrate Numbers!

7

How many
children do you see? ☐

Colour the picture.

Trace the number.

Print the number.

Let's Celebrate Numbers!

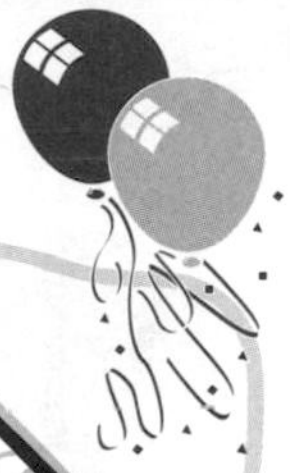

8

How many party hats do you see? ☐

Trace the number.

8 8 8 8 8 8 8 8 8 8 8

8 8 8 8 8 8 8 8 8 8 8

Print the number.

8

8

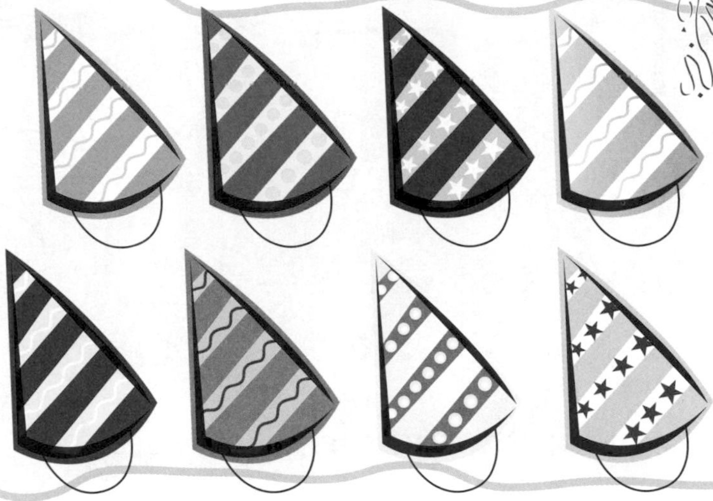

Let's Celebrate Numbers!

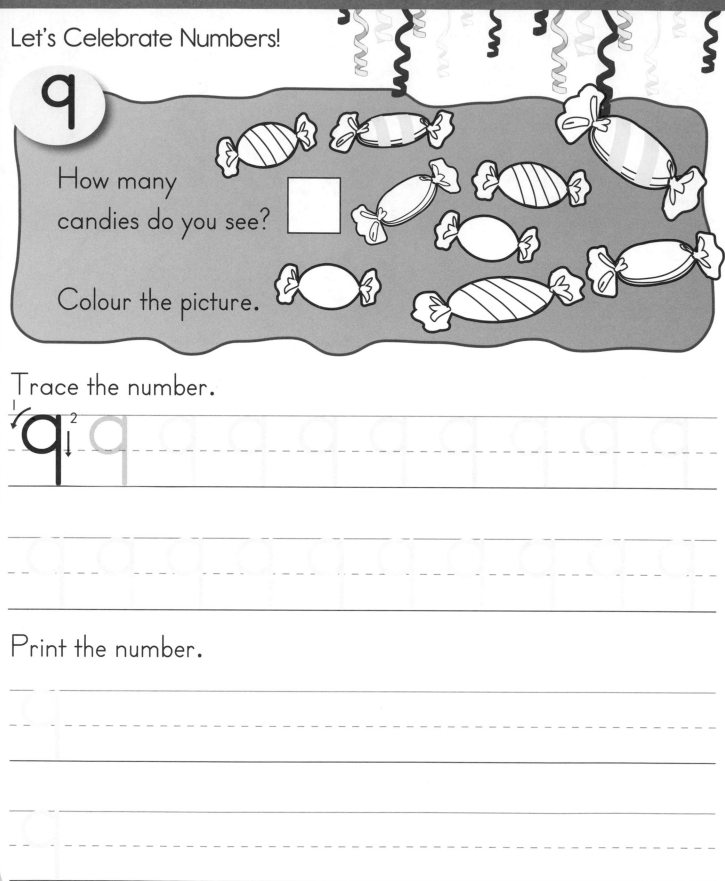

9

How many candies do you see? ☐

Colour the picture.

Trace the number.

Print the number.

Let's Celebrate Numbers!

10

How many bowls of ice cream do you see?

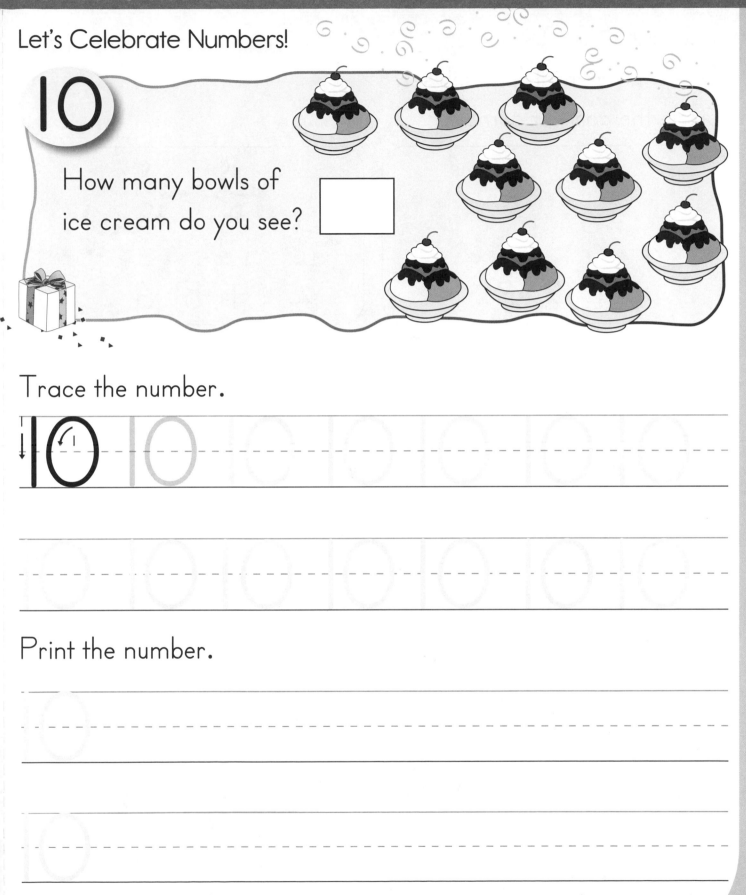

Trace the number.

Print the number.

How Many?

Count the animals in each set.

Circle the correct number.

1 2 3

4 5 6

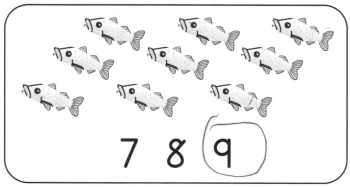

7 8 9

2 3 4

5 6 7

8 9 10

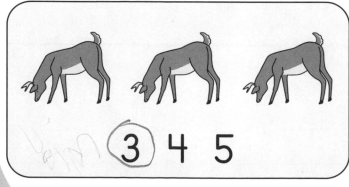

3 4 5

6 7 8

Counting 1 to 10

How many do you see?
Write the number on the line.

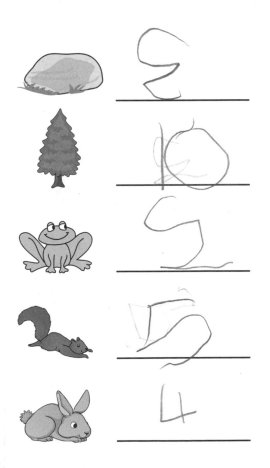

Comparing Numbers

Count and write how many objects are in each group.
Circle the group that has **more.**

How many? 6

How many? 7

How many? 4

How many? 3

Count and write how many objects are in each group.
Circle the group that has **less.**

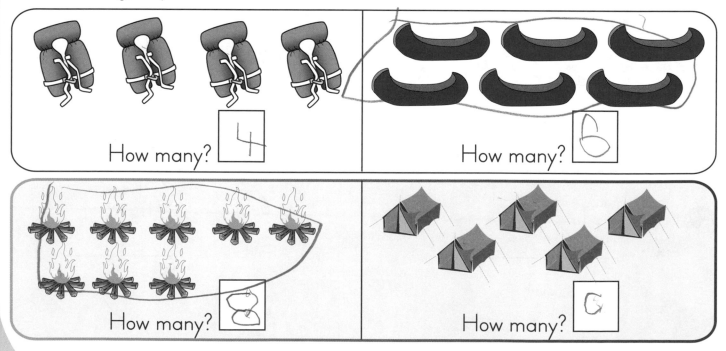

How many? 4

How many? 6

How many? 8

How many? 6

Comparing Numbers

How many of each object is in each set?
Make the number of objects in each set the same by crossing
out objects.

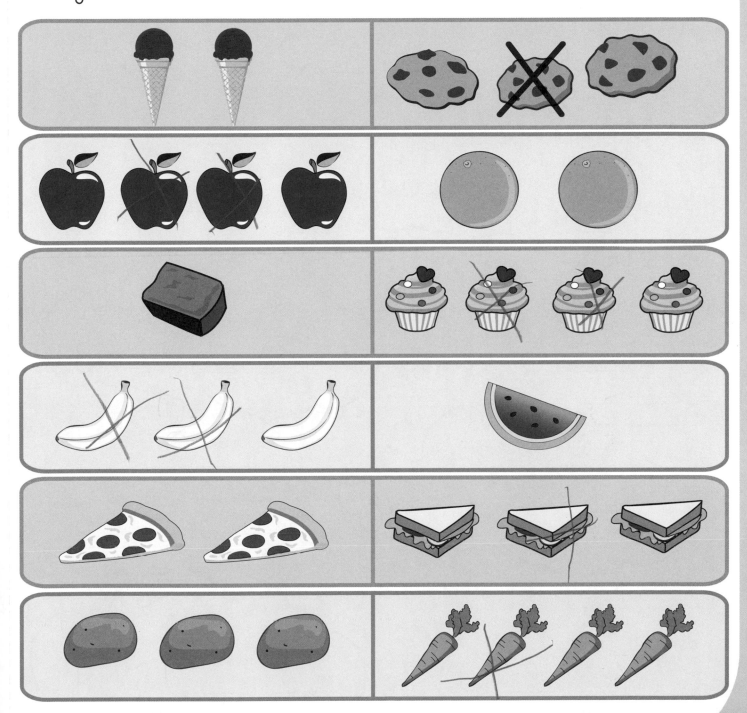

Number Sequence

0 1 2 3 4 5 6 7 8 9 10

Write the number
that comes **before**.   Example: _____ 3 4 5

_____ 3 4

_____ 1 2

_____ 5 6

_____ 2 3

_____ 9 10

_____ 7 8

_____ 6 7

_____ 8 9

Number Sequence

0 1 2 3 4 5 6 7 8 9 10

Write the number
that comes **after.**   Example: 1 2 ___3___

3 4 _____

2 3 _____

6 7 _____

5 6 _____

4 5 _____

8 9 _____

7 8 _____

0 1 _____

0 1 2 3 4 5 6 7 8 9 10

Print the numbers 1 to 10 as you paddle down the river to your camp site.

18

Count Down to Blast Off!

Count the items in each row.

Write the number on the line.

Now count down the numbers and blast off!

Cool Coins

penny	nickel	dime	quarter	dollar	two dollar
1¢	5¢	10¢	25¢	(loonie) $1.00	(toonie) $2.00

Draw a line from the coin to its value.

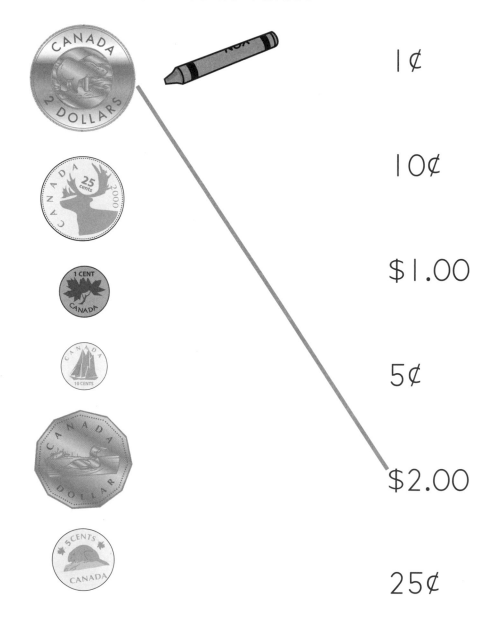

1¢

10¢

$1.00

5¢

$2.00

25¢

Going Shopping

Count the . How many? [ ] ¢

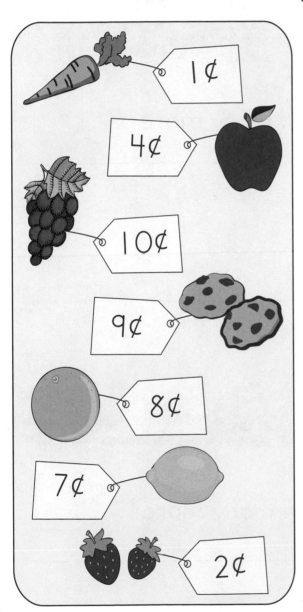

Draw what you could buy.

Put an **X** on the you spend.

How many do you have left? Circle the number.

0¢ 1¢ 2¢ 3¢ 4¢ 5¢ 6¢ 7¢ 8¢ 9¢ 10¢

Adding – How Many?

Put an X on each you count.

How many? ❀ ☐

How many **more**? ❀ ☐

How many ❀ are there now? ☐

How many? 🐦 ☐

How many **more**? 🐦 ☐

How many 🐦 are there now? ☐

Subtracting – How Many?

Put an X on each you count.

How many 🍁 ? ☐

How many 🍁 fell? ☐

Count the 🍁 on the tree.

Now there are ☐ 🍁 on the tree.

How many 🎈 ? ☐

How many 🎈 popped? ☐

Count the 🎈 left.

Now there are ☐ 🎈 .

Counting 11 to 20

Trace the number. Count the dots.
Add dots to make the number.

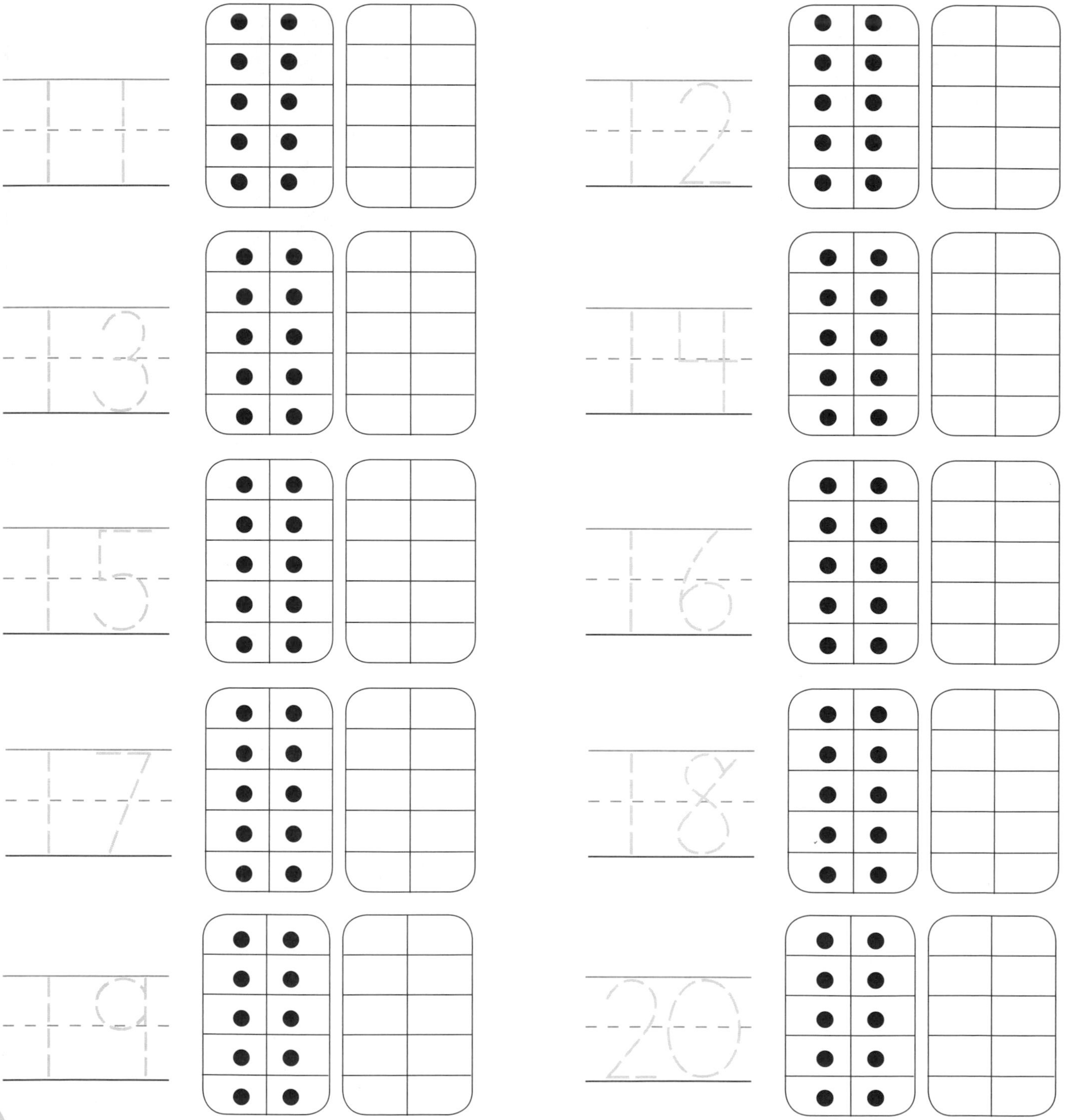

11

12

13

14

15

16

17

18

19

20

Counting 11 to 20

Count the pictures. Circle the matching number.

Hint: Put an **X** on each thing as you count.

One has been started for you.

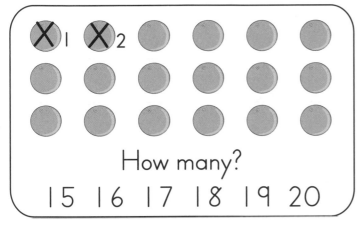

How many?

15   16   17   18   19   20

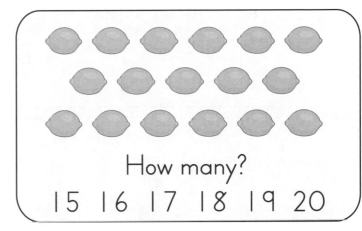

How many?

15   16   17   18   19   20

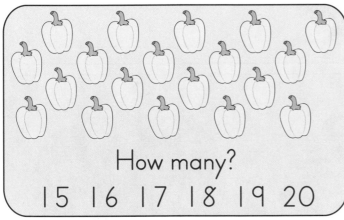

How many?

15   16   17   18   19   20

How many?

15   16   17   18   19   20

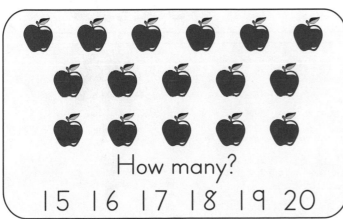

How many?

15   16   17   18   19   20

How many?

15   16   17   18   19   20

Getting Bigger

Draw what is missing.

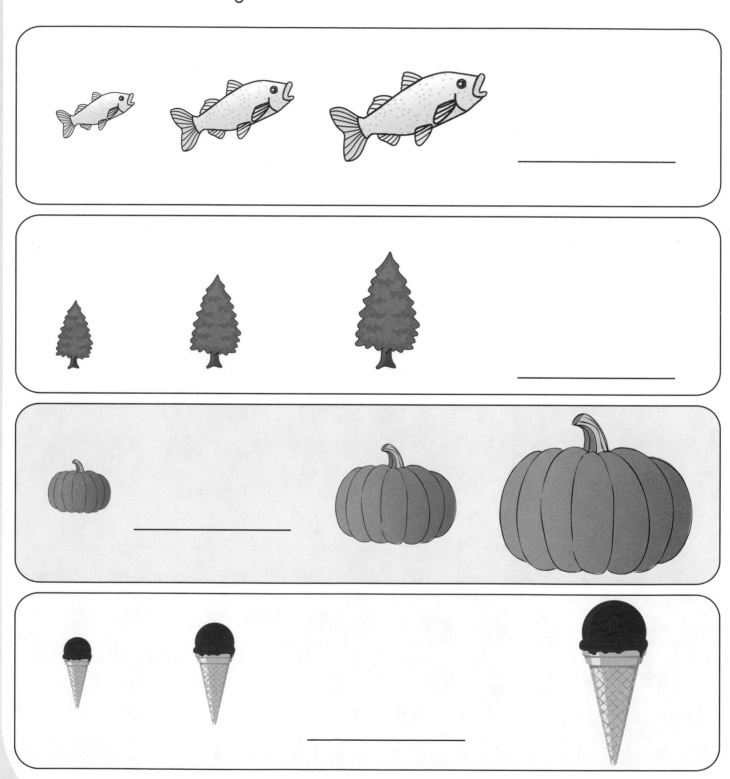

Measuring with Blocks

How many blocks?

How many blocks long is the paintbrush?

How many blocks long is the eraser?

How many blocks long is the fork?

How many blocks long is the crayon?

Measuring with String

It's Time to Measure!

Cut a piece of string as long as your arm.

Find an object longer than the string.

Find an object the same length as the string.

Find an object shorter than the string.

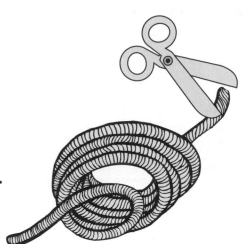

Draw the objects you found.

Longer than the string.	Same length as the string.	Shorter than the string.

Mass: Is it Heavier or Is it Lighter?

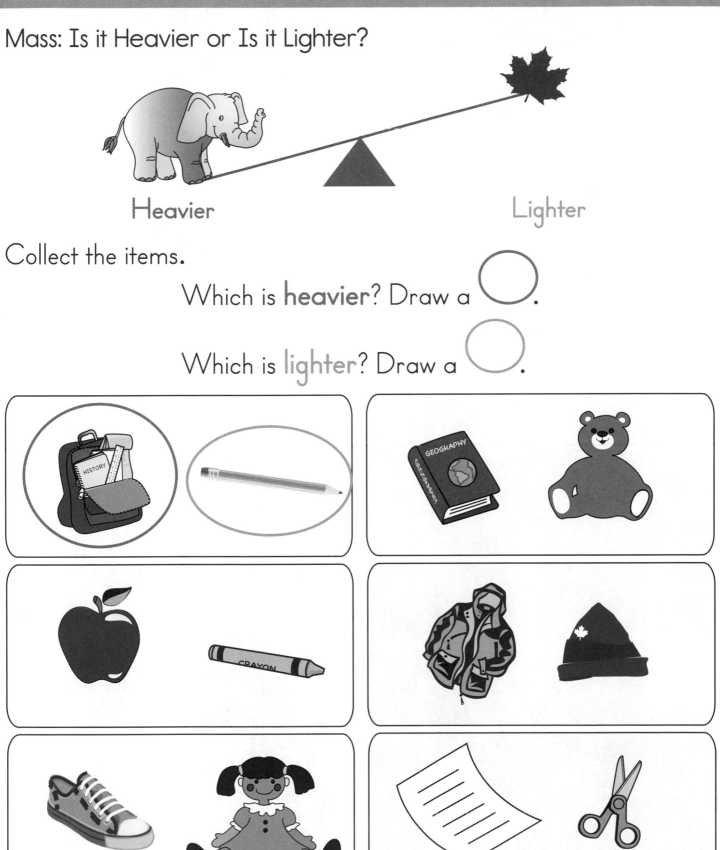

Heavier

Lighter

Collect the items.

Which is **heavier**? Draw a ⬤.

Which is lighter? Draw a ◯.

Mass: Is it Heavy or Is it Light?

Circle the **heavy** objects in blue.
Circle the light objects in green.

Capacity: How Much Does It Hold?

Circle the container that holds the **most.**

Put an **X** on the container that holds the least.

Talking about Time

We measure time with a clock.

The **big hand** tells the **minutes**. Colour the **big hand red**.

The little hand tells the hour. Colour the little hand green.

Trace the numbers. Touch each number and say it out loud.

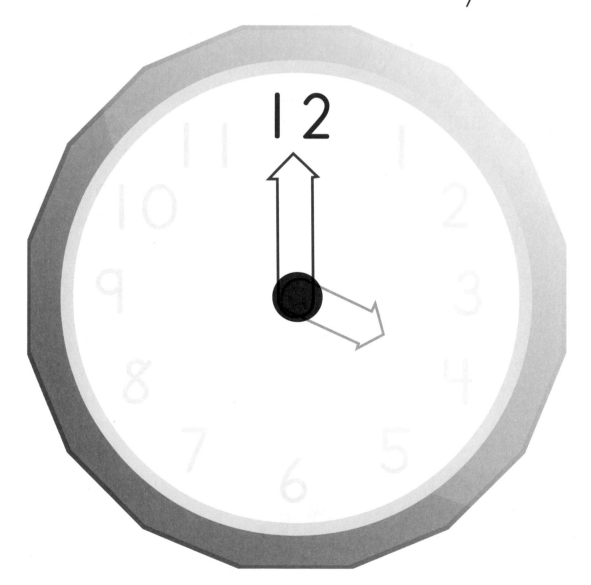

This clock says four o'clock.

My Day – Before and After

Draw what you do **before** school.

Draw what you do after dinner.

On Top, Beside, and Under

The pencil case  is **on top** ⬆ of the desk.

The backpack is **beside** ➡⬅ the desk.

The scissors are **under** ⬇ the desk.

Count:

How many crayons

under ⬇ the desk? ☐

How many backpacks

beside ➡⬅ the desk? ☐

How many pencils

on top ⬆ the desk? ☐

Super 2-D Shapes

Trace each shape with your finger. Say its name.

circle

square

triangle

rectangle

Trace the shape.
Draw the shape.

square 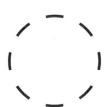	triangle 
circle	rectangle 

Geometry and Spatial Sense

Shape Families

Colour the shapes that belong in each family.

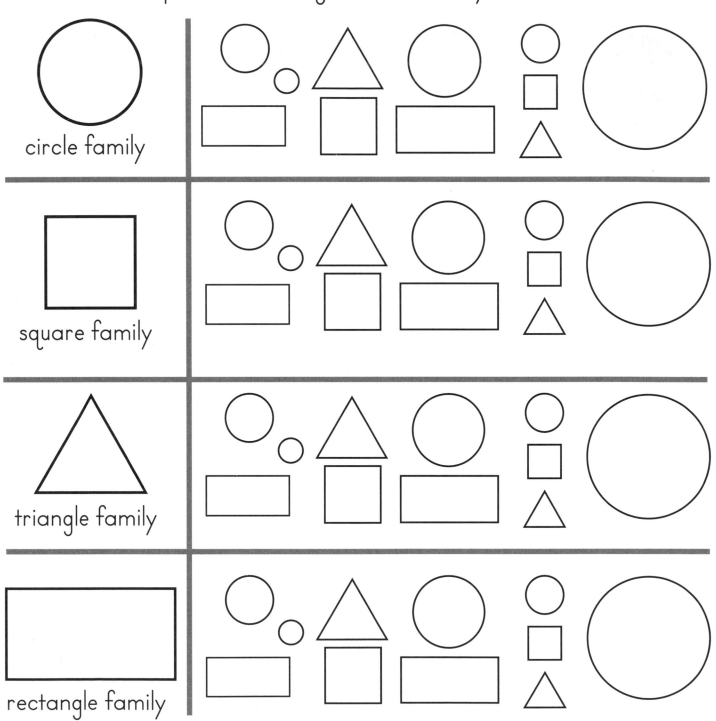

circle family

square family

triangle family

rectangle family

Find the 2-D Shapes

Look at the picture.
Find and count the shapes.

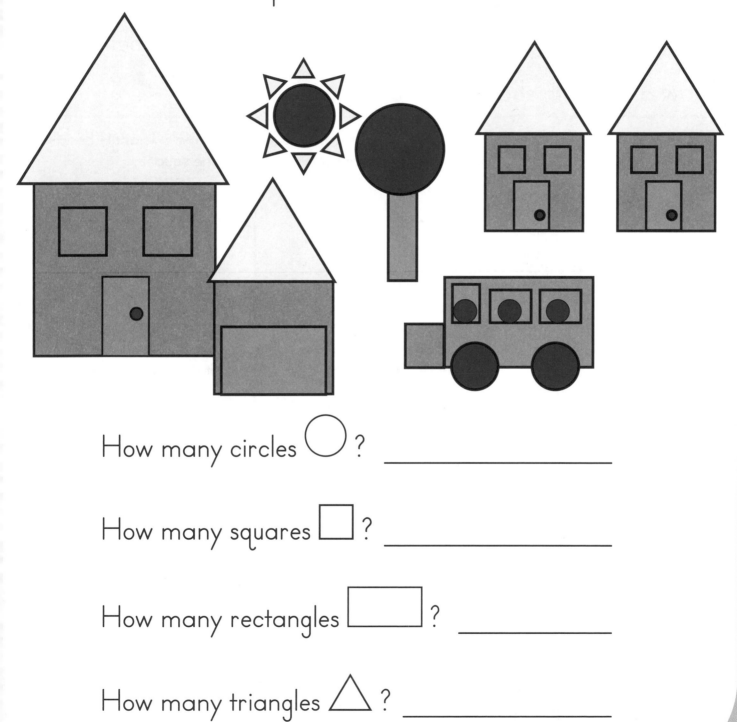

How many circles ○ ? _____

How many squares □ ? _____

How many rectangles ▭ ? _____

How many triangles △ ? _____

Make a Shape Picture

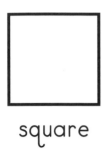   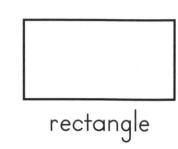

square   circle   triangle   rectangle

Draw a car with shapes

1. Draw a rectangle.	2. Draw 2 squares on top of the rectangle.	3. Draw a triangle beside one square.
	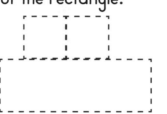	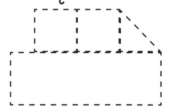
4. Draw 2 circles under the rectangle.	5. Draw 2 more circles inside the squares.	6. Draw 2 small circles at either end of the rectangle.
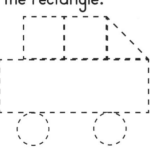	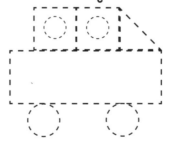	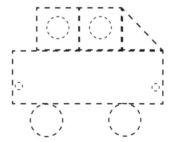

My shape picture has _____ circles ◯.

My shape picture has _____ squares ☐.

My shape picture has _____ triangles △.

My shape picture has _____ rectangles ▭.

3-D Shapes

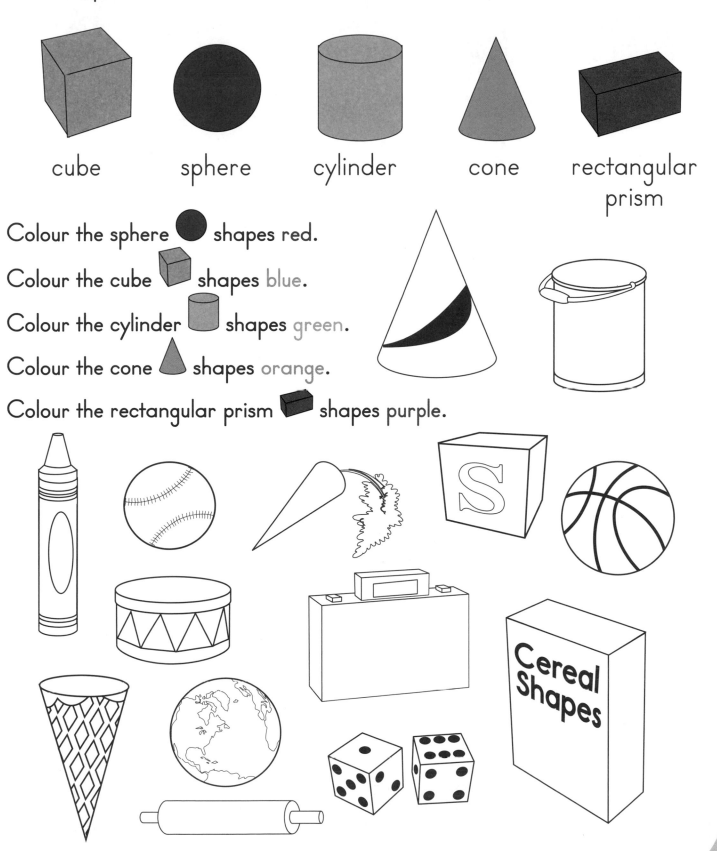

cube　　　sphere　　　cylinder　　　cone　　　rectangular prism

Colour the sphere ● shapes red.

Colour the cube shapes blue.

Colour the cylinder shapes green.

Colour the cone shapes orange.

Colour the rectangular prism shapes purple.

Cereal Shapes

Looking for 3-D Shapes

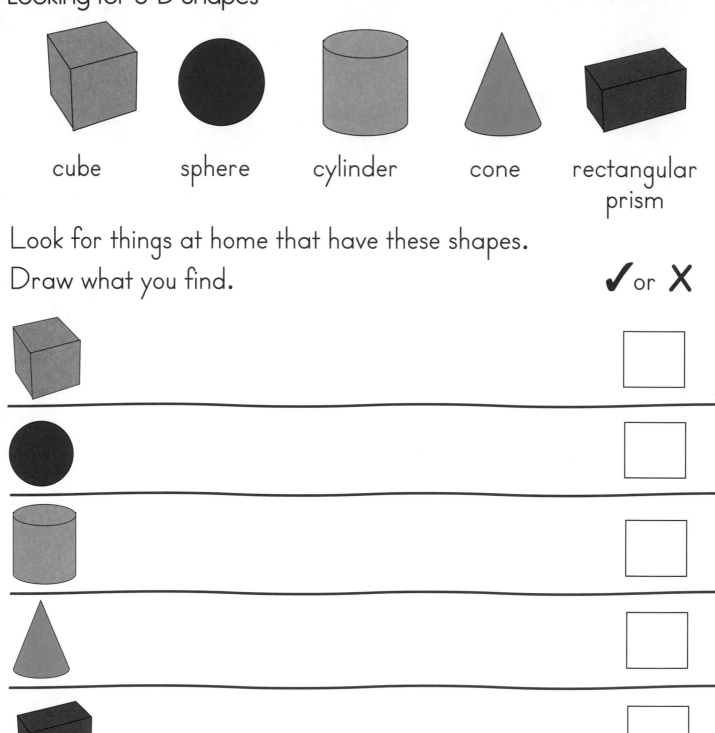

cube   sphere   cylinder   cone   rectangular prism

Look for things at home that have these shapes.
Draw what you find.

✔ or X

Put a ✔ beside the shape you found the **most** of.

Put an **X** beside the shape you found the **least** of.

Does it Stack? Does it Roll?

Put a (blue circle) on things that stack. Put a (green circle) on things that roll. Put **both colours** on things that **stack and roll.**

Colour one square blue for each thing that stacks.

Stack:

How many things stack?

Colour one square green for each thing that rolls.

Roll:

How many things roll?
How many things stack and roll?

41

What Comes Next?

A pattern repeats over and over.
Look at this pattern.
Say the name of the shapes.

Say the things in each pattern. Circle what comes next.

What Comes Next?

Say the things in each pattern. Circle what comes next.

Perfect Patterns

Say the things in each pattern. Circle what comes next.

Patterning

Showing My Patterns Using Letters

We can show patterns in different ways.
Here is a pattern with pictures and letters.

A   B   A   B   A   B   A   B

This is an AB pattern.

Print the letters ABC to show this pattern.

A __   __   __   __   __   __

This is an ABC pattern.

Use letters A B to show this pattern.

__   __   __   __   __   __

Action Patterns

Make these patterns by clapping 🤚, snapping ✊, and 👟 stomping.

Try making different action patterns with your hands and feet.
Say the actions in your patterns. Use letters A B C to tell about the
patterns you made. Print the letters to show the patterns you made.

Example:

A   A   B   A   A   B   A   A   B

My pattern:

Patterning

Make Your Own Patterns

Colour the pictures to make patterns.
Use **blue** and yellow. Use A B to show the pattern you made.

____ ____ ____ ____ ____ ____

Use **red** and **blue**. Use A B to show the pattern you made.

____ ____ ____ ____ ____ ____

Choose your own 3 colours to make a pattern. Use A B C to
show the pattern you made.

____ ____ ____ ____ ____ ____

Make Your Own Patterns

Use to make your own pattern.
Tell what pattern you made.

Patterns are Everywhere!

Look around you. Look for patterns. Look at the patterns on each of these items.

Draw other patterns you see around you.

Look at your favourite shirt.
Does it have a pattern?
Colour the pattern on your shirt.

Super Sorting – Same

Circle the ones in each row that are the **same.**

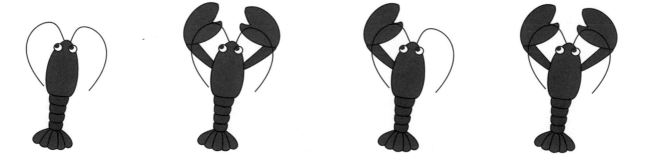

Super Sorting – Different

Sort the fruit. Circle the ones that are different.

Is it Small, Medium, or Large?

Sort the balloons.

Colour the **small** balloons your favourite colour.

Put a ✔ on the **medium** balloons.

Put an **X** on the **large** balloons.

What Goes Together?

Circle the pictures in each group that go together.

What Doesn't Belong?

Draw an **X** on the one that doesn't belong.

Graphing: Our Favourite Fruit

A class took a poll to find out everyone's favourite fruit.

How many children chose each kind of fruit?

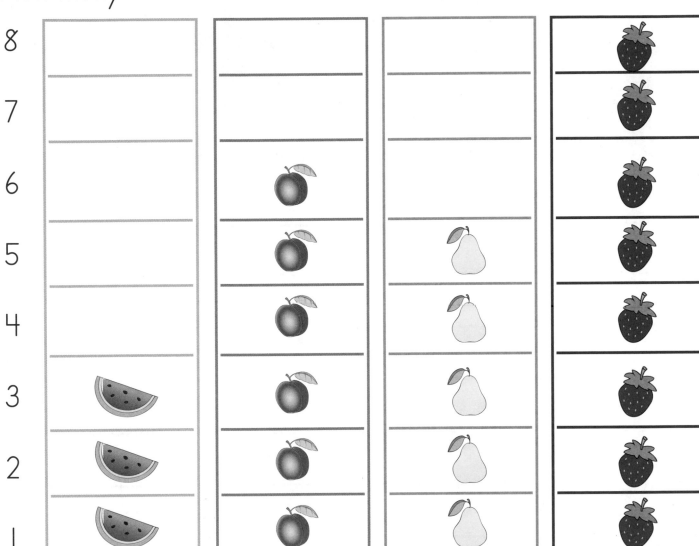

How many 🍉? _____   How many 🍐? _____

How many 🍎? _____   How many 🍓? _____

Circle the **most** popular fruit.

Circle the **least** popular fruit.

Make a Graph

How many of each animal are in the picture?

Colour **one box** for each animal. The is done for you.

7					
6					
5					
4					
3					
2	▨				
1	▨				

Circle the animal there are the most of. Put an **X** on the animal there are the least of.

Heads or Tails?

heads   tails

Flip a penny 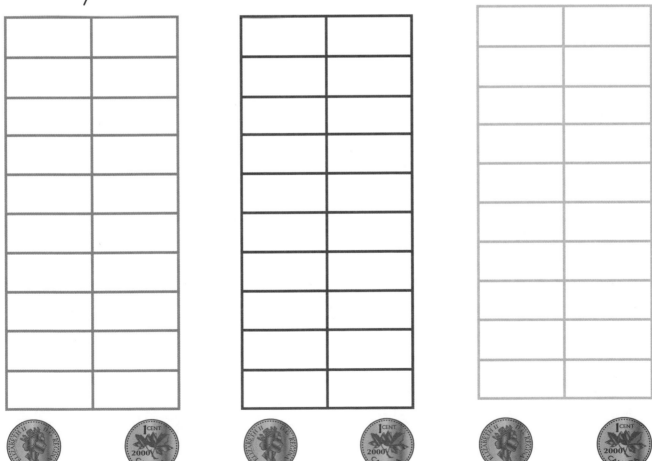 ten times. On the first graph, colour one box

for each flip to show if it landed **heads** or **tails** .

Then flip it 10 more times and colour the second graph.

Last, flip it 10 more times and colour the third graph.

What do you notice?

Solutions

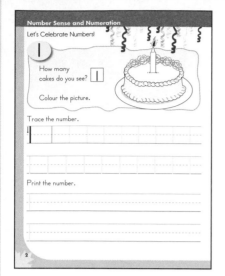

Page 2

Page 3

Page 4

Page 5

Page 6

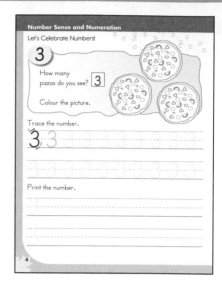

Page 7

Page 8

Page 9

Page 10

Solutions

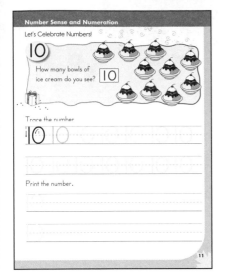

Page 11

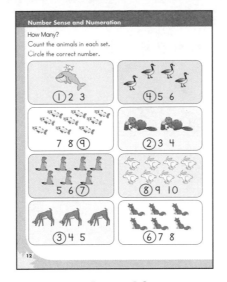

Page 12

Page 13

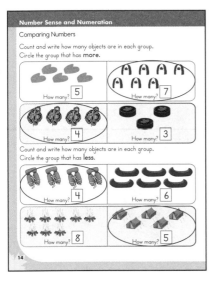

Page 14

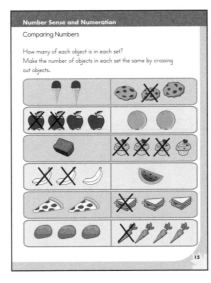

Page 15

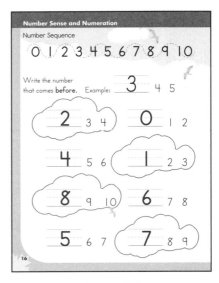

Page 16

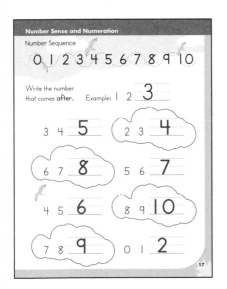

Page 17

Page 18

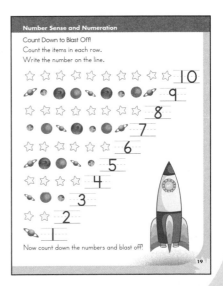

Page 19

Solutions

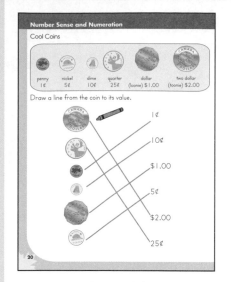

Page 20

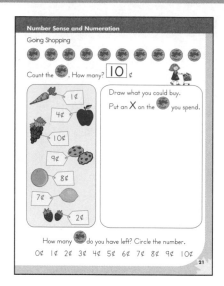

Page 21

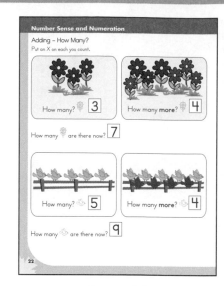

Page 22

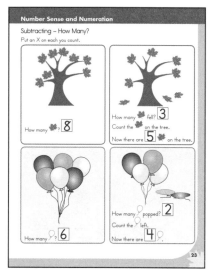

Page 23

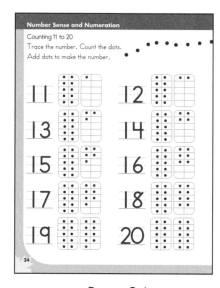

Page 24

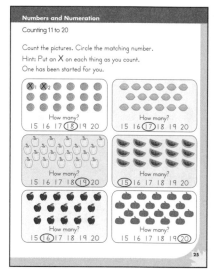

Page 25

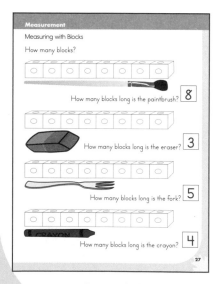

Page 27

Page 29

Page 30

Solutions

Page 31

Page 34

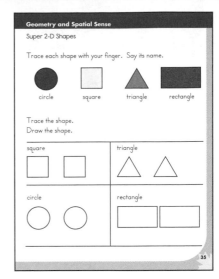

Page 35

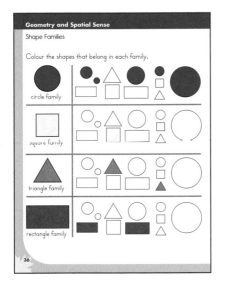

Page 36

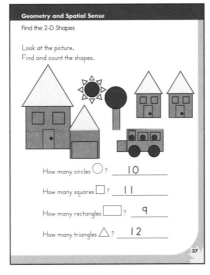

Page 37

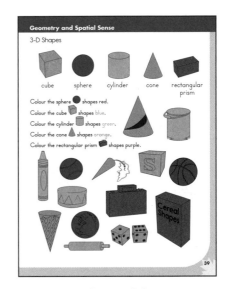

Page 39

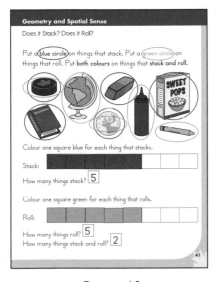

Page 41

Page 42

Page 43

Solutions

Page 44

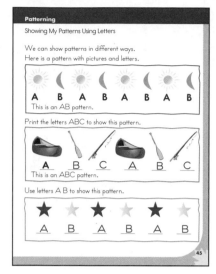

Page 45

Page 50

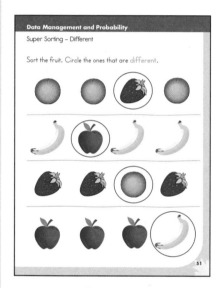

Page 51

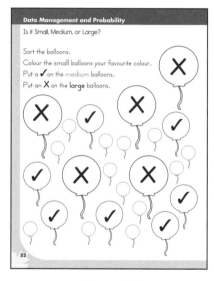

Page 52

Page 53

Page 54

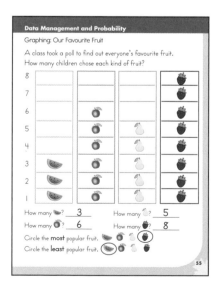

Page 55

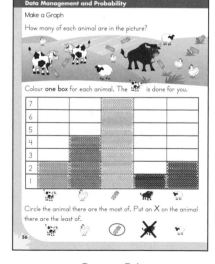

Page 56

Solutions

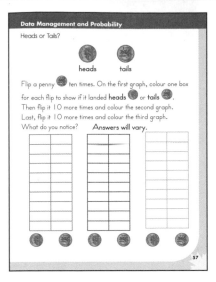
Page 57

Colour Me!